I can go to the top.

You can't top me, little ant. I am a ram!

I am an ant!
I can!

See you
at the top,
little ant!

The ram ran.

The little ant ran.

Go!

A little ant can't top me. I can stop and nap.

The ant ran
on the rocks.

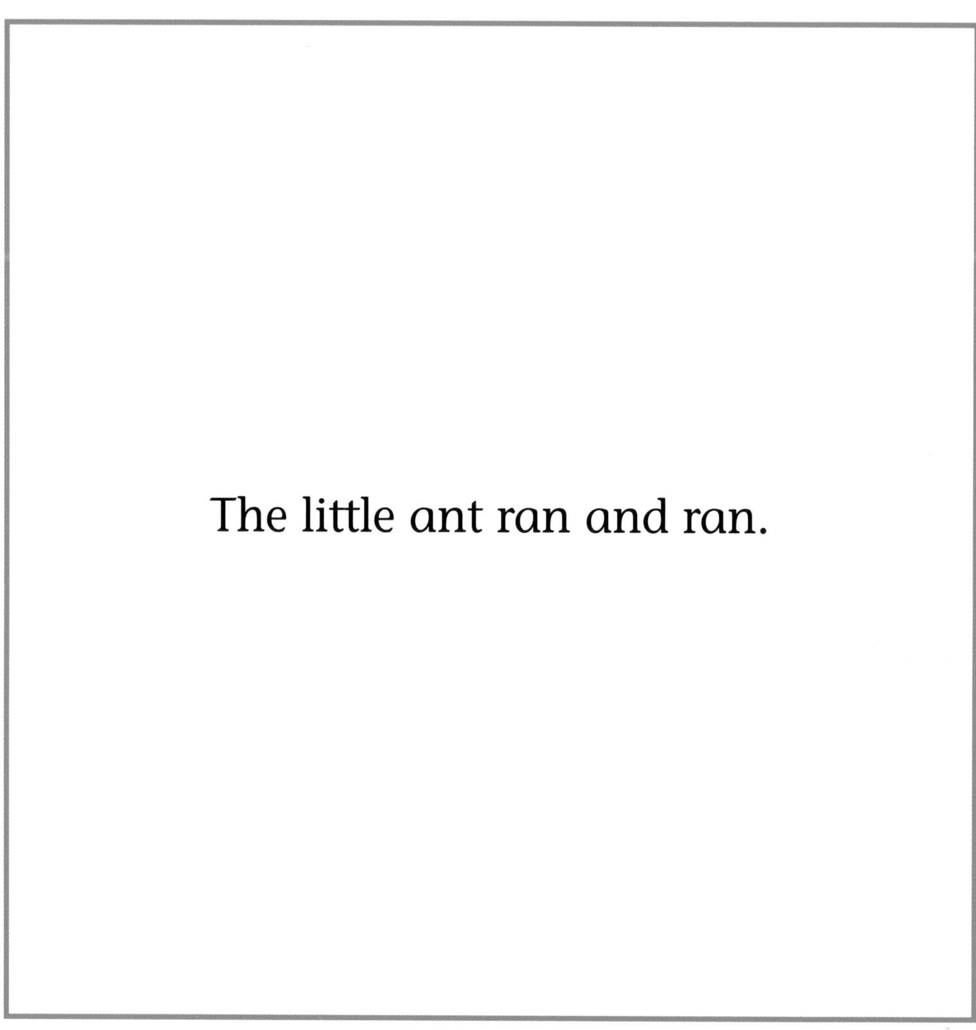

The little ant ran and ran.

The ram can see the ant at the top.

No! Stop!

I did it!
You did it, little ant.

Target Letter-Sound Correspondence

Consonant /r/ sound spelled ***r***

Previously Introduced Letter-Sound Correspondences:

Consonant /s/ sound spelled ***s***
Consonant /m/ sound spelled ***m***
Short /ă/ sound spelled ***a***
Consonant /k/ sound spelled ***c***
Consonant /n/ sound spelled ***n***
Consonant /k/ sound spelled ***k, ck***
Consonant /z/ sound spelled ***s***
Consonant /t/ sound spelled ***t***
Consonant /p/ sound spelled ***p***
Short /ŏ/ sound spelled ***o***
Consonant /g/ sound spelled ***g***
Consonant /d/ sound spelled ***d***
Short /ĭ/ sound spelled ***i***

High-Frequency Puzzle Words

go	see
little	the
me	to
no	you

Bold indicates new high-frequency word.

Decodable Words

a	I
am	it
an	nap
and	on
ant	ram
at	ran
can	rocks
can't	stop
did	top